My Mother-in-Law

The New East Enders Series

Written and illustrated

by Mary Pierce

Gate
HOUSE

My Mother-in-Law
Text & Illustrations copyright © Mary Pierce 2014

Published in 2014 by Gatehouse Media Limited

ISBN: 978-1-84231-093-9

British Library Cataloguing-in-Publication Data:
A catalogue record for this book is available from the British Library

Authors' Note

In 2003 the ESOL Outreach team at Tower Hamlets College gained funding from the East London ESOL Pathfinder to produce a pack of teaching materials relevant to the context of Outreach ESOL classes. Tower Hamlets College was the lead partner for the East London ESOL Pathfinder.

The resulting pack of materials included 6 easy reading booklets for beginning ESOL learners. The reading booklets proved popular and it was suggested that we should try to get them published. We approached Avantibooks who agreed to publish them as a series entitled *The New Eastenders*, but those books are now out of print.

We are delighted that they have now been given a new lease of life by Gatehouse Books as *The New East Enders Series* for a new generation of ESOL learners. We have added a seventh title to the series, called *My Mother-in-Law*, and a useful set of tutor resources and student worksheets. We hope you enjoy using them.

Marta Paluch & Mary Pierce

This is my mother-in-law.
Her name is Rehana Bibi.
She comes from Bangladesh.

This is her husband, Ahmed.
He has got brown eyes, grey hair,
a moustache and a beard.

She is fifty-two years old.
He is sixty-five years old.
My father-in-law is retired.
They live in a flat in Shadwell.
They have got six children -
two sons and four daughters.
They have got ten grandchildren.

My mother-in-law is friendly and helpful.
She likes chatting to the neighbours.

She likes looking after her grandchildren.

They visit her every day.

She gives them sweets and a big hug.

She likes gardening.
She grows coriander and tomatoes.

She likes watching Indian films on television.
She likes romantic films
with singing and dancing.

My mother-in-law is a very good cook.
She helps me with my cooking.

She doesn't like samosas.

She likes chicken biryani.

She likes prawn curry.

She likes fish curry.
Fish curry is her favourite.

Sometimes she is not well.
She has got diabetes.

She has a special diet.
She can't eat sweets or chocolate.
She doesn't like this special diet
because she loves sweet things.

She likes chocolate.

She likes cakes.

She likes ice cream.
It's her favourite dessert.

My mother-in-law likes shopping
in Watney Market.
She goes shopping every day.

I visit my mother-in-law every weekend.
I like my mother-in-law.

If you have enjoyed this book, why not try one of these other titles from *The New East Enders Series:*

A New Home

Fadumo Goes Shopping

From Here to There

Good Neighbours

My Son is Sick

Rima's Day

A comprehensive set of tutor resources is available to support this series of readers:

The New East Enders Series
Tutor Resources CD-ROM

ISBN: 978-1-84231-094-6

Gatehouse Books®

Gatehouse Books are written for older teenagers and adults who are developing their basic reading and writing or English language skills.

The format of our books is clear and uncluttered.
The language is familiar and the text is often line-broken, so that each line ends at a natural pause.

Gatehouse Books are widely used within Adult Basic Education throughout the English speaking world. They are also a valuable resource within the Prison Education Service and Probation Services, Social Services and secondary schools - both in basic skills and ESOL teaching.

Catalogue available

Gatehouse Media Limited
PO Box 965
Warrington
WA4 9DE

Tel/Fax: 01925 267778
E-mail: info@gatehousebooks.com
Website: www.gatehousebooks.com